Conceived and produced by
Breslich & Foss
Golden House
28-31 Great Pulteney Street
London W1R 3DD

Quotations at the beginning of each month are from
The Secret Garden by Frances Hodgson Burnett,
originally published in 1911.

Many of Graham Rust's illustrations originally
appeared in *The Secret Garden* and *The Secret Garden Notebook*,
published by David R. Godine, Publisher.
The remainder are from the artist's collection.

Designed by Peartree Design Associates

ISBN 1 85004 031 1

Sixth Printing 1993

Printed and bound in Hong Kong

THIS IS MY JOURNAL
FOR THE YEAR

19

NAME

_____

ADDRESS

_____

_____

_____

January

*All the ground was covered with grass of a
wintry brown, and out of it grew clumps of bushes
which were surely rose-bushes if they were alive…
There were neither leaves nor roses on them now,
and Mary did not know whether they were dead or alive,
but their thin grey or brown branches and sprays
looked like a sort of hazy mantle spreading
over everything, walls and trees, and even brown grass,
where they had fallen from their fastenings and
run along the ground.*

THOUGHTS FOR

January

MY
FAVORITE
DAY

January

BEST PARTIES
AND
ENTERTAINMENT

January

MY MOST
UNPLEASANT DAY

January

MY FINEST ADVENTURE

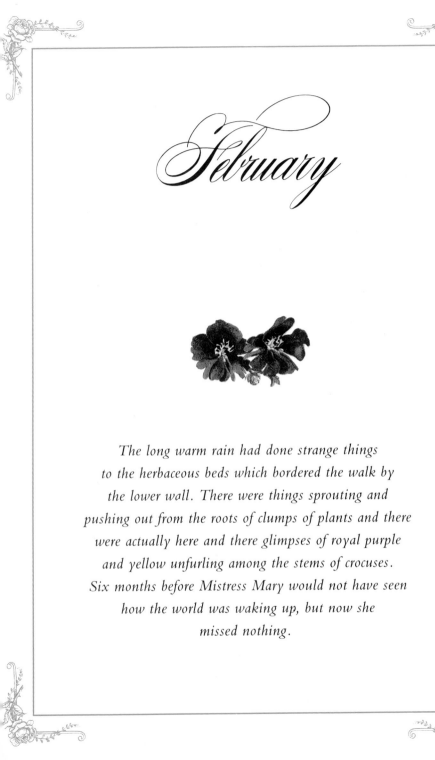

February

The long warm rain had done strange things
to the herbaceous beds which bordered the walk by
the lower wall. There were things sprouting and
pushing out from the roots of clumps of plants and there
were actually here and there glimpses of royal purple
and yellow unfurling among the stems of crocuses.
Six months before Mistress Mary would not have seen
how the world was waking up, but now she
missed nothing.

THOUGHTS FOR
February

MY
FAVORITE
DAY

February

BEST PARTIES
AND
ENTERTAINMENT

February

MY MOST
UNPLEASANT DAY

February

MY FINEST
ADVENTURE

March

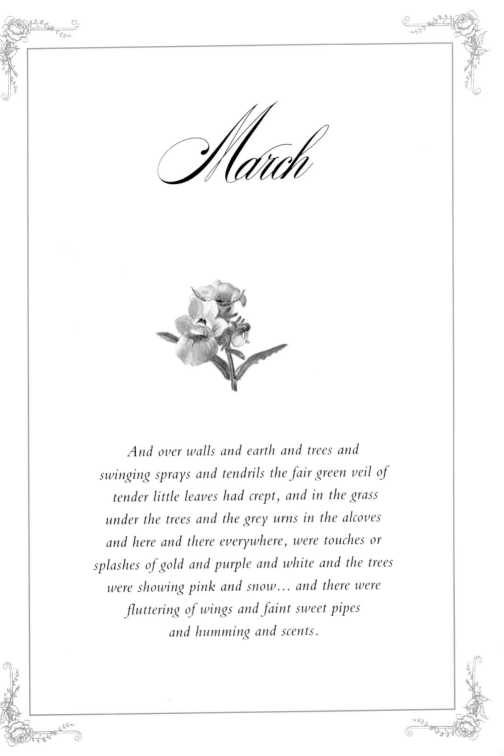

And over walls and earth and trees and
swinging sprays and tendrils the fair green veil of
tender little leaves had crept, and in the grass
under the trees and the grey urns in the alcoves
and here and there everywhere, were touches or
splashes of gold and purple and white and the trees
were showing pink and snow… and there were
fluttering of wings and faint sweet pipes
and humming and scents.

M Y
F A V O R I T E
D A Y

March

BEST PARTIES
AND
ENTERTAINMENT

March

MY MOST
UNPLEASANT DAY

March

MY FINEST
ADVENTURE

April

*At first it seemed that green things would never cease
pushing their way through the earth, in the grass,
in the beds, even in the crevices of the walls.
Then the green things began to show buds, and the buds
began to unfurl and show colour, every shade of blue,
every shade of purple, every tint and hue of crimson...
Irises and white lilies rose out of the grass in sheaves,
and the green alcoves filled themselves with amazing
armies of the blue and white flower lances of tall
delphiniums or columbines or campanulas.*

THOUGHTS FOR

April

MY
FAVORITE
DAY

April

_____

_____

_____

_____

BEST PARTIES
AND
ENTERTAINMENT

_____

_____

_____

_____

April

MY MOST
UNPLEASANT DAY

April

MY FINEST
ADVENTURE

May

*They drew the chair under the plum-tree,
which was snow-white with blossoms and
musical with bees. It was like a king's canopy,
a fairy king's. There were flowering cherry-trees
near and apple-trees whose buds were pink
and white, and here and there one had burst
open wide. Between the blossoming branches of
the canopy bits of blue sky looked down like
wonderful eyes.*

THOUGHTS FOR
May

MY
FAVORITE
DAY

May

BEST PARTIES
AND
ENTERTAINMENT

May

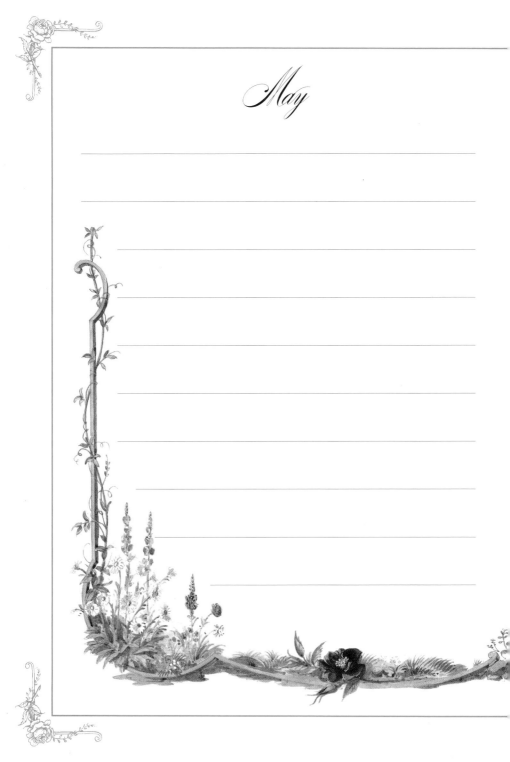

MY MOST
UNPLEASANT DAY

May

MY FINEST
ADVENTURE

June

And the roses - the roses! Rising out of the grass,
tangled round the sun-dial, wreathing the tree-trunks,
and hanging from their branches, climbing up
the walls and spreading over them with long garlands
falling in cascades - they came alive day by day,
hour by hour. Fair, fresh leaves, and buds - and buds -
tiny at first, but swelling and working Magic
until they burst and uncurled into cups of scent
delicately spilling themselves over their brims
and filling the garden air.

THOUGHTS FOR

June

M Y
F A V O R I T E
D A Y

June

BEST PARTIES
AND
ENTERTAINMENT

June

MY MOST
UNPLEASANT DAY

June

MY FINEST
ADVENTURE

July

The rain storm had ended and the grey mist
and clouds had been swept away in the night by
the wind. The wind itself had ceased and a brilliant,
deep blue sky arched high over the moorland.
Never, never had Mary dreamed of a sky so blue.
In India skies were hot and blazing; this was of a deep,
cool blue, which almost seemed to sparkle like the waters
of some lovely, bottomless lake, and here and there,
high, high in the arched blueness, floated small clouds
of snow-white fleece.

THOUGHTS FOR

July

MY
FAVORITE
DAY

July

_____

_____

_____

_____

BEST PARTIES
AND
ENTERTAINMENT

_____

_____

_____

_____

_____

July

MY MOST
UNPLEASANT DAY

July

MY FINEST ADVENTURE

August

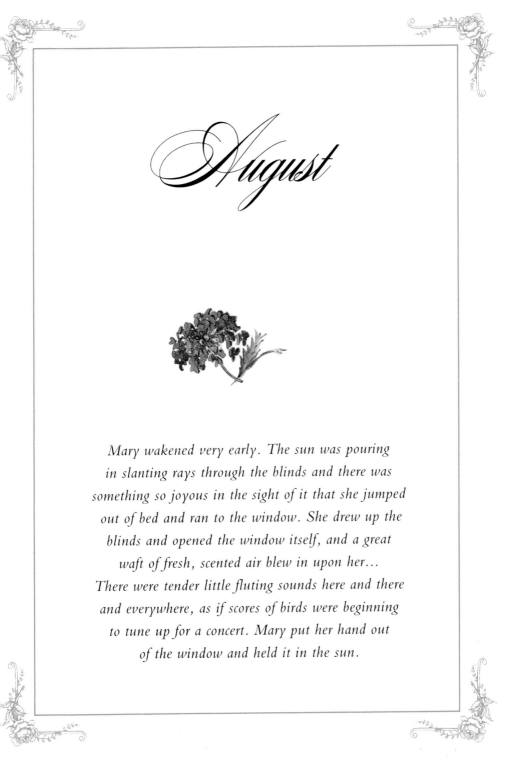

*Mary wakened very early. The sun was pouring
in slanting rays through the blinds and there was
something so joyous in the sight of it that she jumped
out of bed and ran to the window. She drew up the
blinds and opened the window itself, and a great
waft of fresh, scented air blew in upon her...
There were tender little fluting sounds here and there
and everywhere, as if scores of birds were beginning
to tune up for a concert. Mary put her hand out
of the window and held it in the sun.*

THOUGHTS FOR

August

_____

_____

_____

_____

_____

_____

_____

_____

_____

_____

_____

MY
FAVORITE
DAY

August

BEST PARTIES
AND
ENTERTAINMENT

August

MY MOST
UNPLEASANT DAY

_____

_____

_____

_____

_____

_____

_____

_____

_____

_____

August

MY FINEST ADVENTURE

September

*One of the strange things about living in
the world is that it is only now and then one is
quite sure one is going to live for ever and ever
and ever... And one knows it sometimes when one
stands by oneself in a wood at sunset and the
mysterious deep gold stillness slanting through and
under the branches seems to be saying slowly again
and again something one cannot quite hear,
however much one tries.*

THOUGHTS FOR

September

MY
FAVORITE
DAY

September

―――――――――――――――――――――――

―――――――――――――――――――――――

―――――――――――――――――――――――

―――――――――――――――――――――――

BEST PARTIES
AND
ENTERTAINMENT

―――――――――――――――――――――――

―――――――――――――――――――――――

―――――――――――――――――――――――

―――――――――――――――――――――――

―――――――――――――――――――――――

September

MY MOST
UNPLEASANT DAY

September

MY FINEST
ADVENTURE

October

The place was a wilderness of autumn gold
and purple and violet and flaming scarlet, and on
every side were sheaves of late lilies standing together -
lilies which were white or white and ruby.
He remembered well when the first of them had been
planted that just at this season of the year their
late glories should reveal themselves. Late roses climbed
and hung and clustered, and the sunshine deepening
the hue of the yellowing trees made one feel that
one stood in an embowered temple of gold.

THOUGHTS FOR
October

MY
FAVORITE
DAY

October

BEST PARTIES
AND
ENTERTAINMENT

October

MY MOST
UNPLEASANT DAY

October

MY FINEST
ADVENTURE

November

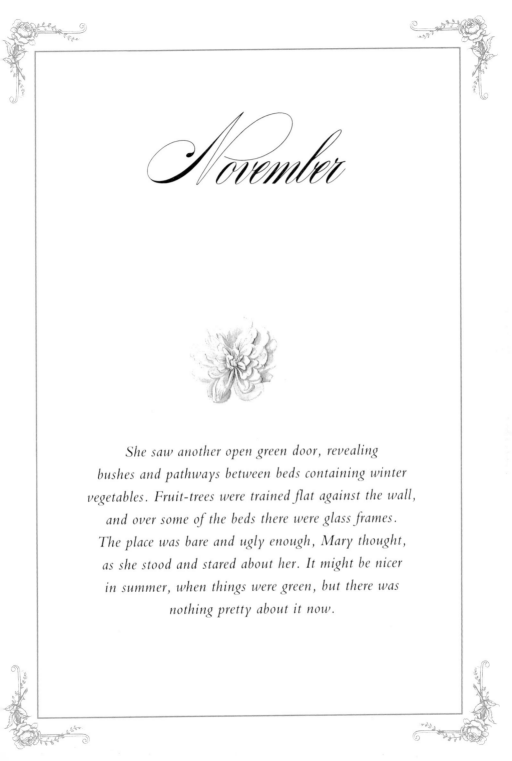

She saw another open green door, revealing
bushes and pathways between beds containing winter
vegetables. Fruit-trees were trained flat against the wall,
and over some of the beds there were glass frames.
The place was bare and ugly enough, Mary thought,
as she stood and stared about her. It might be nicer
in summer, when things were green, but there was
nothing pretty about it now.

THOUGHTS FOR

November

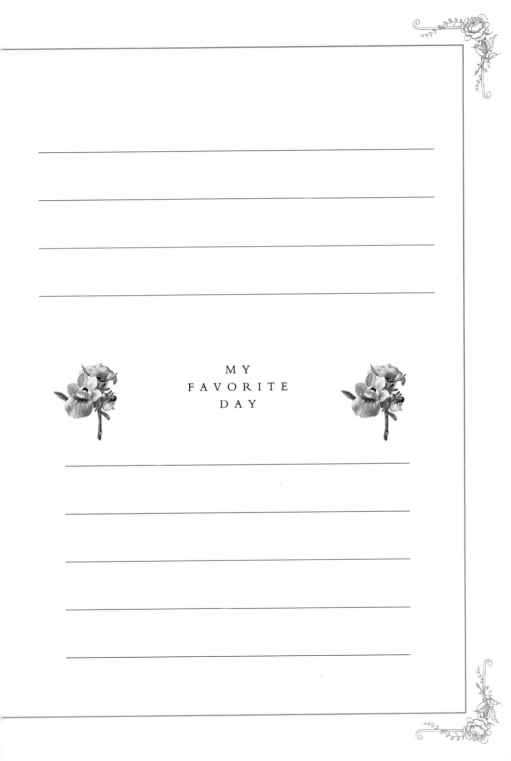

MY
FAVORITE
DAY

November

BEST PARTIES
AND
ENTERTAINMENT

November

MY MOST
UNPLEASANT DAY

November

MY FINEST ADVENTURE

December

She could see the tops of trees above the wall,
and when she stood still she saw a bird with a bright
red breast sitting on the topmost branch of one of them,
and suddenly he burst into his winter song -
almost as if he had caught sight of her and was
calling to her...Almost the next moment a wonderful thing
happened. She heard a soft little rushing flight through
the air - and it was the bird with the red breast
flying to them, and he actually alighted on the big clod
of earth quite near to the gardener's foot.

THOUGHTS FOR

December

MY
FAVORITE
DAY

December

BEST PARTIES
AND
ENTERTAINMENT

December

MY MOST
UNPLEASANT DAY

December

MY FINEST ADVENTURE

NEW YEAR'S
RESOLUTIONS

LAST YEAR'S
RESOLUTIONS
I HAVE KEPT

IMPORTANT   ADDRESSES
AND
TELEPHONE   NUMBERS